THIS JOURNAL BELONGS TO

Introduction

Changes, big and small, are a fact of life. Sometimes we choose to make a change; sometimes a change happens to us. Sometimes we know that change is coming, and sometimes it takes us by surprise. You might be considering a new career path, moving into a new phase of life such as graduation, parenthood, or retirement, or feeling restless and ready for something new. Or you might be grappling with a change that's unexpected—and perhaps unwelcome.

Everyone handles change differently. Self-knowledge is key to navigating periods of transition with as much resilience, authenticity, and happiness as possible.

In this journal, you'll find prompts designed to help you reflect on your experiences, interests, and values so you can move forward in the ways that are right for you.

Onward,

GRETCHEN RUBIN

Done

PROMPT *nº 1*

Write your personal manifesto.

Identify the rules, mottos, or values you want to guide the next chapter in your life.

– **GRETCHEN RUBIN**

/ /

REFLECTIONS

Done

PROMPT *nº 2*

What important lesson have you learned from a challenging situation?

REFLECTIONS

Done

PROMPT *nº 3*

How have your goals and values changed over the course of your life?

.... / .... / ....

REFLECTIONS

Done

PROMPT nº 4

Do you have a lucky charm?

Research suggests that people who believe they have luck on their side feel greater self-efficacy, and this belief actually boosts mental and physical performance.

– GRETCHEN RUBIN

.... / .... / ....

REFLECTIONS

Done

PROMPT *nº 5*

If you're considering a big change, what's standing in your way?

/ /

REFLECTIONS

Done

PROMPT *nº 6*

What in your life gives you the most purpose?

/ /

REFLECTIONS

Done

PROMPT *nº 7*

Imagine yourself five years from now, looking back on this time.

From that vantage point, what will you wish you'd done now?

– **GRETCHEN RUBIN**

REFLECTIONS

Done

PROMPT nº 8

If you could pick any profession and were guaranteed to be successful, what would you choose?

REFLECTIONS

Done

PROMPT *nº 9*

What in your life are you most excited about right now?

/ /

REFLECTIONS

Done

PROMPT *nº 10*

Describe your "fantasy self."

How might you incorporate aspects of your fantasy self into your actual life?

– GRETCHEN RUBIN

/ /

REFLECTIONS

Done

PROMPT *nº 11*

What is your definition of failure?

REFLECTIONS

Done

PROMPT nº 12

What is your definition of success?

.... / .... / ....

REFLECTIONS

Done

PROMPT *nº 13*

Describe your perfect day.

Can you make an ordinary day look more like your perfect day?

– **GRETCHEN RUBIN**

REFLECTIONS

Done

PROMPT *nº 14*

When was the last time you tried something totally new?

/ /

REFLECTIONS

Done

PROMPT *nº 15*

What are you holding onto that you need to let go of?

REFLECTIONS

Done

PROMPT *nº 16*

When dealing with uncertainty, do you often reassure yourself that a decision isn't significant or permanent?

This might sound like, "I might as well," "It can't hurt," "This might be useful," "This will keep my options open," "I can always decide later," "I can always change my mind," "Nothing is forever," "How bad can it be?"

– GRETCHEN RUBIN

REFLECTIONS

Done

PROMPT *nº 17*

What do you find yourself daydreaming about?

REFLECTIONS

Done

PROMPT *nº 18*

What is your level of ambition?

REFLECTIONS

Done

PROMPT *nº 19*

As you face a change, what information would make the transition easier?

What people and resources can help you get the answers you need?

– GRETCHEN RUBIN

REFLECTIONS

■ *Done*

PROMPT *nº 20*

As you think about the future, what's more valuable to you: saving time, energy, or money?

.... / .... / ....

REFLECTIONS

Done

PROMPT *nº 21*

Do you prefer to be a student or a teacher?

.... / .... / ....

REFLECTIONS

Done

PROMPT *nº 22*

Do you give yourself healthy treats—small pleasures that help you to feel comforted and revitalized?

When we give more to ourselves, we can ask more from ourselves, so giving ourselves healthy treats can help us face a challenging transition.

– GRETCHEN RUBIN

/ /

REFLECTIONS

Done

PROMPT *nº 23*

What's your real-life super-power? For example, not suffering from jet lag, remembering names and faces, or having a knack for numbers.

REFLECTIONS

Done

PROMPT *nº 24*

Does it seem like your life is moving forward, sliding backward, or is stuck on hold in some way?

/ /

REFLECTIONS

Done

PROMPT *nº 25*

Looking back, list five actions that you regret (a non-action is an action). What can you learn from those regrets?

While regret can be painful, research shows that it can help us make better decisions, perform better, and bring more meaning to our lives.

– **GRETCHEN RUBIN**

REFLECTIONS

Done

PROMPT *nº 26*

When you look back, what or whom are you grateful for *now* that you didn't feel grateful for *at the time*?

/ /

REFLECTIONS

Done

PROMPT nº 27

What's the best advice you've ever received?

______ / ______ / ______

REFLECTIONS

Done

PROMPT *nº 28*

Do you ever feel weighed down by your possessions?

If so, how might you devote time and energy to clear away some things you no longer need, use, or love?

– **GRETCHEN RUBIN**

/ /

REFLECTIONS

Done

PROMPT *nº 29*

What does freedom look like for you?

REFLECTIONS

Done

PROMPT *nº 30*

With a hobby or activity, do you prefer to refine an existing skill, or try new things?

/ /

REFLECTIONS

Done

PROMPT nº 31

What situation in your life do you most wish had a different outcome?

How would that outcome have improved your life? In what ways is your life better for it not having worked out?

– GRETCHEN RUBIN

REFLECTIONS

Done

PROMPT *nº 32*

If you were going to teach something, what would you teach?

/ /

REFLECTIONS

Done

PROMPT nº 33

Do you feel more like an elderly person looking back on life, or like a kid pretending to be a grown-up?

REFLECTIONS

Done

PROMPT *nº 34*

Are you an alchemist or a leopard?

Alchemists seek ways to change or re-direct their fundamental natures.

Leopards don't try to change their spots—they know who they are, and they don't worry about everything they aren't.

– GRETCHEN RUBIN

______ / ______ / ______

REFLECTIONS

Done

PROMPT nº 35

What do you find yourself complaining about most often?

/ /

REFLECTIONS

Done

PROMPT n° 36

As you face a change, is there a symbol that inspires you?

/ /

REFLECTIONS

Done

PROMPT *nº 37*

How do you deal with pressure?

How do you deal constructively with pressure? Do you have any coping mechanisms that aren't helpful?

– GRETCHEN RUBIN

...... / ...... / ......

REFLECTIONS

Done

PROMPT *nº 38*

Do you tend to expect the worst or believe things will work out?

.... /................ /................

REFLECTIONS

☐ *Done*

PROMPT *nº 39*

If you weren't on the path in life you're on now, what other path might you be following?

.... / .... / ....

REFLECTIONS

Done

PROMPT *nº 40*

Describe your current "season of life."

What do you appreciate about this season of your life? What makes this time different from other times of your life?

– **GRETCHEN RUBIN**

/ /

REFLECTIONS

Done

PROMPT *nº 41*

What sounds more appealing: a peaceful future or an exciting future?

REFLECTIONS

Done

PROMPT *nº 42*

Of all the work you do, what task would you most like to stop doing?

REFLECTIONS

Done

PROMPT *nº 43*

Are you superstitious?

Are there ways that superstitious beliefs shape your actions or thoughts—even when you recognize the superstition?

– **GRETCHEN RUBIN**

REFLECTIONS

Done

PROMPT *nº 44*

Do you prefer to work alone or in the company of other people?

..................../..................../....................

REFLECTIONS

Done

PROMPT nº 45

Do you fantasize that a catastrophe or upheaval will blow up your situation?

/ /

REFLECTIONS

Done

PROMPT *nº 46*

How do you prefer to be supported by others during times of change or uncertainty?

Do you currently have sources of that kind of support?

– GRETCHEN RUBIN

REFLECTIONS

Done

PROMPT *nº 47*

Do you feel like other people or processes are moving events forward, and you're just passively carried along?

REFLECTIONS

Done

PROMPT *nº 48*

If a good friend were in your situation right now, what would you say to them?

.... / .... / ....

REFLECTIONS

Done

PROMPT *nº 49*

How do you learn?

If you want to learn about something new, would you rather take in the information through reading, listening, or watching?

What's a new topic that you would like to learn more about?

– **GRETCHEN RUBIN**

REFLECTIONS

Done

PROMPT *nº 50*

Do you find yourself doing or getting something because the people around you are doing it or want it?

REFLECTIONS

Done

PROMPT *nº 51*

Is there anything in your life about which you used to be passionate, but now you never allow yourself to enjoy?

REFLECTIONS

Done

PROMPT nº 52

What's the worst that could realistically happen?

How would you handle that outcome?

– GRETCHEN RUBIN

REFLECTIONS

Done

PROMPT *nº 53*

What's the best possible outcome?

.... / .... / ....

REFLECTIONS

Done

PROMPT *nº 54*

From what mistake have you learned the most?

/ /

REFLECTIONS

Done

PROMPT *nº 55*

What were you like as a child?

What childhood qualities or traits do you still have? What qualities or traits have you lost that you wish you still had?

– **GRETCHEN RUBIN**

/ /

REFLECTIONS

Done

PROMPT *nº 56*

When do you feel most alive?

REFLECTIONS

Done

PROMPT *nº 57*

What is the most challenging thing you're dealing with right now?

.... / .... / ....

REFLECTIONS

Done

PROMPT *nº 58*

Do you spend a lot of time on something that's important to someone else, but not to you?

If the project has a natural end, how could you avoid picking up similar responsibilities in the future? If it is an on-going responsibility, is there someone else who would be more enthusiastic about it?

– GRETCHEN RUBIN

.... / .... / ....

REFLECTIONS

☐ *Done*

PROMPT *nº 59*

Change, whether good and bad, can be stressful. Check in with your body. How are you feeling?

/ /

REFLECTIONS

Done

PROMPT *nº 60*

What habit or activity consistently makes you feel happier, healthier, or grounded?

REFLECTIONS

About Gretchen Rubin

Gretchen Rubin is one of the most thought-provoking and influential writers on the linked subjects of habits, happiness, and human nature. She's the author of many blockbuster *New York Times* bestselling books, including *The Happiness Project* and *Better Than Before*. Her books have sold more than three million copies worldwide, in more than thirty languages. On her award-winning podcast, *Happier with Gretchen Rubin*, she shares insights, strategies, stories, and tips that help people understand themselves and create happier lives. Gretchen started her career in law and was clerking for Supreme Court Justice Sandra Day O'Connor when she realized she wanted to be a writer. She lives in New York City with her husband and two daughters.

To learn more about happiness, habits, and human nature, follow **@gretchenrubin** on social media and sign up for Gretchen's newsletter at **gretchenrubin.com**.

Resources

BOOKS

Gretchen Rubin is the author of many bestselling books on happiness, habits, and human nature. She combines rigorous research with personal observation to help readers know themselves better, and become happier, healthier, more productive, and more creative.

Better Than Before

What I Learned About Making and Breaking Habits—to Sleep More, Quit Sugar, Procrastinate Less, and Generally Build a Happier Life

The Happiness Project

Or, Why I Spent a Year Trying to Sing in the Morning, Clean My Closets, Fight Right, Read Aristotle, and Generally Have More Fun

The Four Tendencies

The Indispensable Personality Profiles That Reveal How to Make Your Life Better (and Other People's Lives Better, Too)

Happier at Home

Kiss More, Jump More, Abandon Self-Control, and My Other Experiments in Everyday Life

Outer Order, Inner Calm

Declutter and Organize to Make More Room for Happiness

WEBSITE

Explore Gretchen's popular blog on happiness and habits, read author interviews, and download helpful resources. You can also sign up to receive her free weekly newsletter (with more than one million subscribers), blog updates, podcast show notes, and daily "Moment of Happiness" emails.

Visit gretchenrubin.com.

PODCAST

Every week on *Happier with Gretchen Rubin*, Gretchen brings her practical, manageable insights about happiness and good habits to this lively, thought-provoking podcast. Gretchen's co-host is her younger sister, Elizabeth Craft, a TV writer and producer, who (lovingly) refers to Gretchen as her happiness bully. They explore a wide range of topics, from quick happiness hacks to fascinating discoveries about human nature.

APP

The *Happier*™ app is the practical toolbox to help you start your own Happiness Project and build the habits to create the life you want. Get strategies tailored specifically to you, using Gretchen Rubin's research- and observation-based principles to determine the approach that's most likely to set you up for success.

Download at thehappierapp.com, or from the Apple App Store and Google Play.

THE
HAPPINESS
PROJECT

GRETCHEN RUBIN

the-happiness-project.com | gretchenrubin.com

Cover artist: Baiko Pirtskhalaishvili